LUDWIG VAN

T0069592

QUARTET

for 2 Violins, Viola and Violoncello
E minor/e-Moll/Mi mineur
Op. 59/2

Edited by/Herausgegeben von
Wilhelm Altmann

Ernst Eulenburg Ltd

London · Mainz · Madrid · New York · Paris · Prague · Tokyo · Toronto · Zürich

BEETHOVEN
STRING QUARTET IN E MINOR, OP. 59 No. 2

In the year 1802 Beethoven had followed the String Quartets op. 18 with a Quartet arrangement of the E major Piano Sonata op. 14, but several years passed before he entered again into the composition of original String Quartets. The private inducement was a commission made to him by the amateur Graf Rasumovsky, the Russian ambassador in Vienna at that time.

The autograph copy of this 2nd Quartet, which for a long time has been in the possession of the Royal Library in Berlin bears Beethoven's inscription: – Quartetto 1mo La prima parte solamente una volta – Quartetto angefangen(begun)26.May1806.

The composition of these Quartets which were not generally appreciated at the time occupied Beethoven together with his other works op. 56, 57, 58 and also 60; they were completed by the end of 1806. According to the custom then in vogue they remained unpublished for a year, the property of the person who had commissioned them and to whom they were dedicated. On Nov. 18th 1806 Beethoven offered them to Breitkopf & Härtel in Leipzig for the sum of 600 florins, but without success. It is uncertain which is the original edition. According to Dugge these Quartets appeared in Jan. 1808 under the title: – Trois Quatuors pour deux Violons, Alto e Violoncelle. Composés par Louis van Beethoven. Oeuvre 59me Livraison 1, bzw. 2, 3 à Vienne au Magazin de J. Riedl. 582. Hohenmarkt. (Stich-No. 580, 584, 585.) But Nottebohm gives the publication as: "Vienne au Bureau des arts et d'industrie à Pesth chez Schreyvogel & Comp." with the same publication number. The latter is probably correct; the firm of Johann Riedl in Vienna, which went out of existence about 1829, may have taken the quartets over from the Bureau.

The third page of the cover of the Riedl (probably the original) edition is adorned with the Rasumovsky coat of arms: Famam extendere factis; under which stands the following dedication: –

Trois Quatuors Très humblement Dediés à son Excellence Monsieur le Comte De Rasoumoffsky Conseiller privé actuel de Sa Majesté L'Empereur De Toutes Les Russies, Senateur, Chevalier des ordres de Saint André, de Saint Alexandre-Newsky et Grand-Croix de celui de Saint Wladimir de la première Classe etc. etc. par Louis van Beethoven.

The metronome marks were added later by the composer.

In honour of Count Rasumovsky, Beethoven has introduced a Russian folk-song into the first and second quartet. The Russian theme used in the Trio of the Scherzo in No. 2 occurs in the collection of Russian tunes by Ivan Pratsch, which Beethoven knew in the following form (see G. Nottebohm, Second Beethoveniana 90):

Andante.

This popular song has been used by M. Mussorgsky in his opera "Boris Godunow" (finished 1872), also by A. Arensky in a string quartet op. 35 (1894), and by Wassily Zolotarew in a string quintet op. 19 (1905).

Prof. Dr. Wilh. Altmann

BEETHOVEN
STREICHQUARTETT IN E MOLL, OP. 59 No. 2

Zwar hatte Beethoven im Jahre 1802 seinen 1801 erschienenen Streichquartetten op. 18 die Umarbeitung der E-dur-Klaviersonate op. 14 Nr. 1 in ein Quartett (in F dur) folgen lassen, allein es vergingen mehrere Jahre, bis er wieder an die Komposition von Originalstreichquartetten ging. Die äußere Veranlassung dazu war ein Auftrag oder Wunsch des kunstliebenden Grafen Rasumovsky, des damaligen russischen Botschafters in Wien.

Das Autograph dieses II. Quartettes, seit längerer Zeit im Besitze der Musiksammlung der Königl. Bibliothek zu Berlin, ist von Beethoven überschrieben: Quartetto 1mo La prima parte solamente una volta — Quartetto angefangen am 26. May 1806.

Die Komposition dieser Quartette, die von den Zeitgenossen zuerst nicht recht gewürdigt worden sind, beschäftigte Beethoven neben seinen Werken 56, 57, 58 und auch 60; sie waren am Ende des Jahres 1806 vollendet. Der Sitte der Zeit nach blieben sie ein Jahr lang ungedruckt im Besitze des Auftraggebers, dem sie auch gewidmet wurden. Am 18. November 1806 bot sie Beethoven der Firma Breitkopf & Härtel in Leipzig für 600 Gulden vergeblich zum Verlag an. Nicht ganz aufgeklärt ist, welches die Originalausgabe ist. Nach Herrn Dugges Ansicht sind diese Quartette im Januar 1808 erschienen, und zwar unter dem Titel: Trois Quatuois pour deux Violons, Alto e Violoncelle. Composés par Louis van Beethoven. Oeuvre 59me Livraison 1, bzw. 2, 3 à Vienne au Magazin de J. Riedl. 582. Hohenmarkt. (Stich-No. 580, 584, 585.) Nottebohm aber gibt als Verlag „Vienne au Bureau des arts et d'industrie à Pesth chez Schreyvogel & Comp." mit den gleichen Verlagsnummern an. Er hat wohl recht; ich glaube, daß die ca. 1829 erloschene Firma Johann Riedl in Wien diese Quartette von dem Bureau übernommen hat.

Die dritte Umschlagseite dieser Riedlschen (und wohl auch der ursprünglichen) Ausgabe ist mit dem Wappen der Rasumovsky — der Wahlspruch lautet: Famam extendere factis — geschmückt, unter welchem folgende Widmung steht:

Trois Quatuors Très humblement Dediés à son Excellence Monsieur le Comte De Rasoumoffsky Conseiller privé actuel de Sa Majesté L'Empereur De Toutes Les Russies, Senateur, Chevalier des ordres de Saint André, de Saint Alexandre-Newsky et Grand-Croix de celui de Saint Wladimir de la première Classe &tc. &tc. par Louis van Beethoven.

Die Metronomisierung ist später von Beethoven festgesetzt worden.

Dem Grafen Rasumovsky zu Ehren hat Beethoven in dem ersten und zweiten Quartett je ein russisches Volkslied eingeflochten. Das im Trio des Scherzos von No. 2 verwendete russische Thema erscheint in der von Iwan Pratsch herausgegebenen Sammlung russischer Volkslieder, die Beethoven gekannt hat (vgl. G. Nottebohm, Zweite Beethoveniana 90), in folgender Gestalt:

Andante.

Dieses Volkslied ist als Krönungshymne von M. Mussorgsky in seiner Oper „Boris Godunow" (vollendet 1874) verwendet worden. Verwertet ist es ferner von Anton Arensky in einem Streichquartett op. 35 (1894) und von Wassily Kolotarew in einem Streichquartett op. 19 (1905).

Prof. Dr. Wilh. Altmann

Quartet

I

Ludwig van Beethoven, Op. 59. N? 2.
1770-1827

N? 29.

E.E. 1129

E. E. 1129

E.E. 1129

E.E. 1129

9

10

180

E. E. 1129

E.E.1129

14

250

II

Molto Adagio. Si tratta questo pezzo con molto di sentimento. ♩= 60

10

E.E.1129

29

16

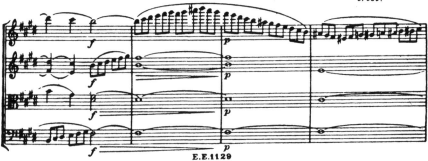

18

E.E.1129

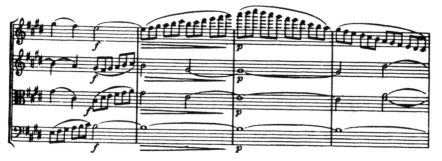

E.E.1129

III

Allegretto. $\d. = 69$

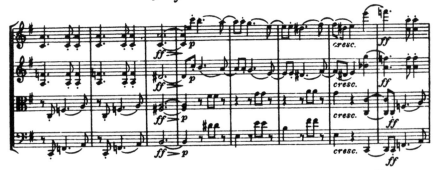

Maggiore

Thème russe

Thème russe

E. E. 1129

26

E E 1129

Da capo il minore ma senza replica ed allora ancora una
volta il trio, e dopo di nuovo da capo il minore senza replica.

Finale
Presto ○ = 88 (♩ = 176)

IV

32

E.E.1129

E.E. 1129

E. E. 1129

E. E. 1129

42

E.E.1129

Più presto. o = 112

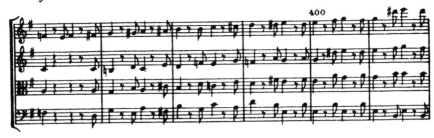